Gordon

CLARINET FOLK-WEAVE

Ten unaccompanied pieces,
mixing traditional and jazz, for
the more accomplished player

**The Associated Board of
the Royal Schools of Music**

NOCHE FLAMENCA

GORDON LEWIN

Andalusian flamenco – known as 'Cante Jondo' and usually interpreted through voice, guitar and dance – is here transcribed for solo wind instrument in the style of the Zorongo and Seguiriya gitana.

AB 2330

THE LOWLAND LASSIE

The yellowing pages of an old Scottish Country Fiddler's Book from 1850 yielded the three tunes ('Flowers of Edinburgh', 'Harvest's Home' and 'Donald') which form this piece.

AB 2330

MOLTO BENNY

Benny Goodman has probably had a greater impact on clarinettists of this century than any other player. His influence on the jazz scene was immeasurable. With his trio and quartet he made 'Chamber Jazz' his own, and his commissioning of serious works has vastly enriched the concert repertoire. This jazz piece pays affectionate tribute to his many recordings.

8

LE PETIT SAVOYARD

An old French folk tune from the High Alps is here treated as a theme and variations in the 19th-century style of Baermann and Klose.

THE KLEZMER'S HORA

'Klezmer' – originally two Hebrew words ('Klay Zemer') meaning an instrument of tune or song – is now the name given to both the itinerant folk musicians and the music of the Jews of Eastern Europe. 'Hora' is a round dance of Eastern European origin, usually of a celebratory nature, popular in Greece and Rumania, and now virtually the national dance of Israel.

A DISTANT SHORE

During the swing era the world of jazz clarinettists was divided into the followers of Artie Shaw and Benny Goodman. Although retiring from active playing in the mid-50s, Artie Shaw's music still retains its fresh inventiveness and originality, while his lyrical style has influenced two whole generations of players. This piece is by way of salutation.

AB 2330

AB 2330

WELTSCHMERZ

This piece is a bitter-sweet evocation of Vienna, as if the last piece of Sachertorte has finally been relinquished by Johann Strauss to Gustav Mahler.

BRAZILLIANCE

This samba, with its pushing two-beat rhythm, contains jazz-influenced phraseology.

FRANCO-FILED

For jazz clarinet players the natural successor to the swinging Goodman and the romantic Shaw was the bop-inspired Buddy de Franco. Forging a new style, his incredible technical virtuosity has been an inspiration to clarinettists worldwide. This piece is a small act of homage.

THE DANDY O

This Irish folk tune from the 19th century provides a touch of the blarney in some of the implied harmonies.

Printed in England by Caligraving Limited Thetford Norfolk   AB 2330   6:93